Addition and Subtraction
using
Expanded Written Methods

A Photocopiable Activity Book by:
Helen Maden and Jane Lambert

Introduction

The four rules of number are the foundation of numeracy work in the Primary School. Curriculum 2000 for Mathematics details how emphasis should be placed on developing the knowledge and understanding of mental calculations, then progressing to more formal written calculations.

The National Numeracy Strategy's Framework for teaching mathematics outlines how expanded versions of more formal written methods should be taught so that children fully understand their methods rather than carrying them out 'by rote'.

This book will take your children 'Step by Step' through these expanded methods in Addition and Subtraction leading them to a greater understanding of more formal vertical layouts.

Other books in this series include:
Multiplication & Division (using Expanded Written Methods)
4 Rules of Number (for compact calculation practice)
Facts at Your Fingertips 1 (for addition and subtraction within 20)
Facts at Your Fingertips 2 (for multiplication and division facts)

Topical Resouces publishes a range of Educational Materials for use in Primary Schools and Pre-School Nurseries and Playgroups.

For latest catalogue:
Tel: 01772 863158
Fax: 01772 866153

E.Mail: sales@topical-resources.co.uk
Visit our Website on:
www.topical-resources.co.uk

Printed in Great Britain for "Topical Resources", Publishers of Educational Materials, P.O. Box 329, Broughton, Preston, PR3 5LT by T.Snape & Company Ltd, Boltons Court, Preston, England.

Typeset by Paul Sealey Illustration and Design, 3 Wentworth Drive, Thornton, England. FY5 5AR.

First Published January 2004
ISBN 1 872977 80 4

Contents

Name:_____ Date:_____

Exercise 1   Addition - Basic Mental Methods

1. $7 + 2 =$ 9 so $70 + 20 =$ 90

2. $6 + 2 =$ [ ] so $60 + 20 =$ [ ]

3. $4 + 3 =$ [ ] so $40 + 30 =$ [ ]

4. $2 + 4 =$ [ ] so $20 + 40 =$ [ ]

5. $8 + 1 =$ [ ] so $80 + 10 =$ [ ]

6. $2 + 5 =$ [ ] so $20 + 50 =$ [ ]

7. $5 + 4 =$ [ ] so $50 + 40 =$ [ ]

8. $3 + 6 =$ [ ] so $30 + 60 =$ [ ]

9. $4 + 5 =$ [ ] so $40 + 50 =$ [ ]

10. $2 + 6 =$ [ ] so $20 + 60 =$ [ ]

Exercise 2   Addition - Basic Mental Methods

1. $6 + 8 =$ 14 so $60 + 80 =$ 140

2. $7 + 6 =$ [ ] so $70 + 60 =$ [ ]

3. $4 + 9 =$ [ ] so $40 + 90 =$ [ ]

4. $8 + 8 =$ [ ] so $80 + 80 =$ [ ]

5. $5 + 8 =$ [ ] so $50 + 80 =$ [ ]

6. $9 + 4 =$ [ ] so $90 + 40 =$ [ ]

7. $7 + 7 =$ [ ] so $70 + 70 =$ [ ]

8. $3 + 8 =$ [ ] so $30 + 80 =$ [ ]

9. $6 + 6 =$ [ ] so $60 + 60 =$ [ ]

10. $3 + 7 =$ [ ] so $30 + 70 =$ [ ]

Name:_____ Date:_____

Exercise 3   Addition - Basic Mental Methods

1   60 + 10 = $\boxed{70}$

2   40 + 10 = $\boxed{}$

3   70 + 10 = $\boxed{}$

4   30 + 10 = $\boxed{}$

5   140 + 10 = $\boxed{}$

6   20 + 10 = $\boxed{}$

7   170 + 10 = $\boxed{}$

8   100 + 10 = $\boxed{}$

9   50 + 10 = $\boxed{}$

10   130 + 10 = $\boxed{}$

11   80 + 10 = $\boxed{}$

12   150 + 10 = $\boxed{}$

13   190 + 10 = $\boxed{}$

14   160 + 10 = $\boxed{}$

15   90 + 10 = $\boxed{}$

16   110 + 10 = $\boxed{}$

Exercise 4   Addition - Basic Mental Methods

1   40 + 17 = $\boxed{57}$

2   70 + 13 = $\boxed{}$

3   20 + 14 = $\boxed{}$

4   80 + 18 = $\boxed{}$

5   50 + 15 = $\boxed{}$

6   30 + 12 = $\boxed{}$

7   140 + 16 = $\boxed{}$

8   170 + 13 = $\boxed{}$

9   110 + 18 = $\boxed{}$

10   150 + 12 = $\boxed{}$

11   130 + 16 = $\boxed{}$

12   170 + 13 = $\boxed{}$

13   140 + 17 = $\boxed{}$

14   120 + 14 = $\boxed{}$

15   110 + 18 = $\boxed{}$

16   160 + 15 = $\boxed{}$

Name:_____ Date:_____

Exercise 5   Addition - Mental Methods Using Jottings

1   42 + 25   =   (2 + 5)   +   (40 + 20)   =

                        7   +   60   = | 67 |

2   46 + 21   =   (   )   +   (   )   =

                              +   = | ___ |

3   34 + 61   =   (   )   +   (   )   =

                              +   = | ___ |

4   73 + 22   =   (   )   +   (   )   =

                              +   = | ___ |

5   42 + 54   =   (   )   +   (   )   =

                              +   = | ___ |

6   37 + 50   =   (   )   +   (   )   =

                              +   = | ___ |

7   28 + 61   =   (   )   +   (   )   =

                              +   = | ___ |

Name:_____ Date:_____

Exercise 6 Addition - Mental Methods Using Jottings

1 38 + 49   =   (8 + 9)   +   (30 + 40)   =

                         17   +   70   = | 87 |

---

2 47 + 38   =   (   )   +   (   )   =

                               +   = | |

---

3 65 + 27   =   (   )   +   (   )   =

                               +   = | |

---

4 51 + 39   =   (   )   +   (   )   =

                               +   = | |

---

5 48 + 26   =   (   )   +   (   )   =

                               +   = | |

---

6 36 + 56   =   (   )   +   (   )   =

                               +   = | |

---

7 29 + 43   =   (   )   +   (   )   =

                               +   = | |

Name:_____ Date:_____

Exercise 7   Addition - Mental Methods Using Jottings

1   62 + 75   =   (5 + 2)   +   (60 + 70)   =

        7   +   130   = | 137 |

---

2   86 + 42   =   (   )   +   (   )   =

                     +   = | |

---

3   94 + 83   =   (   )   +   (   )   =

                     +   = | |

---

4   74 + 94   =   (   )   +   (   )   =

                     +   = | |

---

5   73 + 50   =   (   )   +   (   )   =

                     +   = | |

---

6   64 + 75   =   (   )   +   (   )   =

                     +   = | |

---

7   82 + 41   =   (   )   +   (   )   =

                     +   = | |

Name:_____ Date:_____

Exercise 8 Addition - Mental Methods Using Jottings

1 69 + 78   =   (9 + 8)   +   (60 + 70)   =

                         17   +   130   = | 147 |

2 78 + 63   =   (   )   +   (   )   =

                                    +   = | |

3 56 + 79   =   (   )   +   (   )   =

                                    +   = | |

4 67 + 89   =   (   )   +   (   )   =

                                    +   = | |

5 48 + 65   =   (   )   +   (   )   =

                                    +   = | |

6 96 + 75   =   (   )   +   (   )   =

                                    +   = | |

7 67 + 86   =   (   )   +   (   )   =

                                    +   = | |

Name:_____ Date:_____

Exercise 9   Addition - Mental Methods Using Minimal Jottings

1 43 + 21 = (3 + 1) + (40 + 20) = 64

2 42 + 36 = (   ) + (   ) = [ ]

3 27 + 41 = (   ) + (   ) = [ ]

4 51 + 38 = (   ) + (   ) = [ ]

5 22 + 65 = (   ) + (   ) = [ ]

6 73 + 24 = (   ) + (   ) = [ ]

7 62 + 25 = (   ) + (   ) = [ ]

8 31 + 37 = (   ) + (   ) = [ ]

9 53 + 36 = (   ) + (   ) = [ ]

10 45 + 24 = (   ) + (   ) = [ ]

11 82 + 16 = (   ) + (   ) = [ ]

12 26 + 43 = (   ) + (   ) = [ ]

13 64 + 24 = (   ) + (   ) = [ ]

14 27 + 42 = (   ) + (   ) = [ ]

15 54 + 25 = (   ) + (   ) = [ ]

16 66 + 23 = (   ) + (   ) = [ ]

17 26 + 33 = (   ) + (   ) = [ ]

18 54 + 40 = (   ) + (   ) = [ ]

19 32 + 27 = (   ) + (   ) = [ ]

20 46 + 32 = (   ) + (   ) = [ ]

21 21 + 76 = (   ) + (   ) = [ ]

22 35 + 54 = (   ) + (   ) = [ ]

23 41 + 23 = (   ) + (   ) = [ ]

Name:_____ Date: _____

Exercise 10 Addition - Mental Methods Using Minimal Jottings

1 38 + 47 = (8 + 7) + (30 + 40) = | 85 |

2 26 + 35 = (   ) + (   ) = [   ]

3 42 + 29 = (   ) + (   ) = [   ]

4 54 + 38 = (   ) + (   ) = [   ]

5 37 + 55 = (   ) + (   ) = [   ]

6 63 + 28 = (   ) + (   ) = [   ]

7 58 + 37 = (   ) + (   ) = [   ]

8 22 + 68 = (   ) + (   ) = [   ]

9 39 + 53 = (   ) + (   ) = [   ]

10 43 + 28 = (   ) + (   ) = [   ]

11 57 + 34 = (   ) + (   ) = [   ]

12 63 + 28 = (   ) + (   ) = [   ]

13 23 + 67 = (   ) + (   ) = [   ]

14 34 + 47 = (   ) + (   ) = [   ]

15 45 + 36 = (   ) + (   ) = [   ]

16 56 + 27 = (   ) + (   ) = [   ]

17 62 + 28 = (   ) + (   ) = [   ]

18 24 + 68 = (   ) + (   ) = [   ]

19 35 + 48 = (   ) + (   ) = [   ]

20 44 + 27 = (   ) + (   ) = [   ]

21 55 + 36 = (   ) + (   ) = [   ]

22 66 + 28 = (   ) + (   ) = [   ]

23 46 + 39 = (   ) + (   ) = [   ]

Exercise 11 Addition - Mental Methods Using Minimal Jottings

#	Problem							
1	75 + 41	=	(6)	+	(110)	=	116
2	86 + 23	=	( )	+	( )	=	
3	64 + 55	=	( )	+	( )	=	
4	58 + 71	=	( )	+	( )	=	
5	42 + 83	=	( )	+	( )	=	
6	78 + 61	=	( )	+	( )	=	
7	42 + 84	=	( )	+	( )	=	
8	71 + 68	=	( )	+	( )	=	
9	27 + 82	=	( )	+	( )	=	
10	35 + 84	=	( )	+	( )	=	
11	66 + 53	=	( )	+	( )	=	
12	32 + 94	=	( )	+	( )	=	
13	54 + 73	=	( )	+	( )	=	
14	62 + 53	=	( )	+	( )	=	
15	47 + 62	=	( )	+	( )	=	
16	56 + 73	=	( )	+	( )	=	
17	38 + 81	=	( )	+	( )	=	
18	76 + 42	=	( )	+	( )	=	
19	21 + 94	=	( )	+	( )	=	
20	30 + 87	=	( )	+	( )	=	
21	48 + 71	=	( )	+	( )	=	
22	26 + 83	=	( )	+	( )	=	
23	31 + 86	=	( )	+	( )	=	

Name:_____ Date:_____

Exercise 12 Addition - Mental Methods Using Minimal Jottings

1   67 + 89   =   (16)   +   (140)   = | 156 |

2   74 + 68   =   (   )   +   (   )   =

3   38 + 74   =   (   )   +   (   )   =

4   26 + 85   =   (   )   +   (   )   =

5   42 + 78   =   (   )   +   (   )   =

6   65 + 76   =   (   )   +   (   )   =

7   59 + 65   =   (   )   +   (   )   =

8   43 + 78   =   (   )   +   (   )   =

9   84 + 68   =   (   )   +   (   )   =

10   72 + 69   =   (   )   +   (   )   =

11   37 + 85   =   (   )   +   (   )   =

12   78 + 65   =   (   )   +   (   )   =

13   82 + 48   =   (   )   +   (   )   =

14   56 + 75   =   (   )   +   (   )   =

15   38 + 84   =   (   )   +   (   )   =

16   88 + 55   =   (   )   +   (   )   =

17   46 + 75   =   (   )   +   (   )   =

18   73 + 68   =   (   )   +   (   )   =

19   68 + 76   =   (   )   +   (   )   =

20   28 + 87   =   (   )   +   (   )   =

21   45 + 69   =   (   )   +   (   )   =

22   57 + 77   =   (   )   +   (   )   =

23   83 + 38   =   (   )   +   (   )   =

Name:_____ Date:_____

Exercise 13 Addition - Expanded Version

1
```
    4 2
 +  2 5
 _____
      7
    6 0
 _____
    6 7
 _____
```

2
```
    4 6
 +  3 3
 _____

 _____
```

3
```
    7 1
 +  2 4
 _____

 _____
```

4
```
    4 3
 +  3 3
 _____

 _____
```

5
```
    2 4
 +  6 1
 _____

 _____
```

6
```
    4 3
 +  2 6
 _____

 _____

 _____
```

7
```
    8 4
 +  1 3
 _____

 _____

 _____
```

8
```
    5 6
 +  3 2
 _____

 _____

 _____
```

9
```
    6 5
 +  2 2
 _____

 _____

 _____
```

10
```
    3 6
 +  2 3
 _____

 _____

 _____
```

11
```
    4 2
 +  3 6
 _____

 _____

 _____
```

12
```
    5 5
 +  4 2
 _____

 _____

 _____
```

13
```
    7 2
 +  2 7
 _____

 _____

 _____
```

14
```
    2 5
 +  5 4
 _____

 _____

 _____
```

15
```
    3 6
 +  4 3
 _____

 _____

 _____
```

16
```
    6 6
 +  2 3
 _____

 _____

 _____
```

17
```
    7 1
 +  2 5
 _____

 _____

 _____
```

18
```
    6 4
 +  2 5
 _____

 _____

 _____
```

19
```
    2 1
 +  7 8
 _____

 _____

 _____
```

20
```
    3 9
 +  4 0
 _____

 _____

 _____
```

Name:_____ Date:_____

Exercise 14 Addition - Expanded Version

1
```
   2 6
 + 3 7
 _____
   1 3
   5 0
 _____
   6 3
 _____
```

2
```
   3 8
 + 4 6
 _____

 _____
```

3
```
   3 6
 + 4 7
 _____

 _____
```

4
```
   4 8
 + 2 2
 _____

 _____
```

5
```
   2 7
 + 4 9
 _____

 _____
```

6
```
   2 7
 + 3 4
 _____

 _____
```

7
```
   5 4
 + 2 6
 _____

 _____
```

8
```
   3 5
 + 4 5
 _____

 _____
```

9
```
   2 8
 + 5 6
 _____

 _____
```

10
```
   4 7
 + 3 4
 _____

 _____
```

11
```
   5 7
 + 3 8
 _____

 _____
```

12
```
   2 9
 + 6 3
 _____

 _____
```

13
```
   3 8
 + 2 9
 _____

 _____
```

14
```
   3 5
 + 4 7
 _____

 _____
```

15
```
   6 8
 + 2 3
 _____

 _____
```

16
```
   6 3
 + 2 8
 _____

 _____
```

17
```
   4 6
 + 3 8
 _____

 _____
```

18
```
   5 9
 + 2 7
 _____

 _____
```

19
```
   4 3
 + 3 9
 _____

 _____
```

20
```
   2 7
 + 6 5
 _____

 _____
```

Name:_____ Date:_____

Exercise 15 Addition - Expanded Version

1
```
    7 2
+   9 4
--------
      6
  1 6 0
--------
  1 6 6
```

2
```
    8 4
+   2 2
--------

--------
```

3
```
    6 3
+   7 4
--------

--------
```

4
```
    8 3
+   4 6
--------

--------
```

5
```
    6 2
+   7 3
--------

--------
```

6
```
    8 4
+   7 3
--------

--------
```

7
```
    6 6
+   7 3
--------

--------
```

8
```
    9 5
+   5 4
--------

--------
```

9
```
    3 7
+   8 2
--------

--------
```

10
```
    8 2
+   4 6
--------

--------
```

11
```
    6 7
+   5 2
--------

--------
```

12
```
    6 3
+   7 4
--------

--------
```

13
```
    5 5
+   6 3
--------

--------
```

14
```
    8 4
+   4 5
--------

--------
```

15
```
    2 7
+   9 0
--------

--------
```

16
```
    3 8
+   8 1
--------

--------
```

17
```
    7 4
+   5 4
--------

--------
```

18
```
    2 6
+   8 3
--------

--------
```

19
```
    5 5
+   7 2
--------

--------
```

20
```
    6 7
+   7 2
--------

--------
```

Name:_____ Date:_____

Exercise 16 Addition - Expanded Version

1
```
    6 9
+   7 8
-------
    1 7
  1 3 0
-------
  1 4 7
```

2
```
    7 8
+   4 3
-------
```

3
```
    8 4
+   4 8
-------
```

4
```
    9 6
+   7 5
-------
```

5
```
    8 3
+   7 9
-------
```

6
```
    5 5
+   7 8
-------
```

7
```
    3 9
+   8 4
-------
```

8
```
    6 7
+   7 5
-------
```

9
```
    4 2
+   8 8
-------
```

10
```
    3 7
+   8 5
-------
```

11
```
    5 4
+   8 8
-------
```

12
```
    2 1
+   8 9
-------
```

13
```
    3 6
+   7 7
-------
```

14
```
    4 3
+   7 9
-------
```

15
```
    8 2
+   3 9
-------
```

16
```
    7 7
+   6 5
-------
```

17
```
    5 9
+   7 5
-------
```

18
```
    6 4
+   8 7
-------
```

19
```
    4 8
+   7 8
-------
```

20
```
    5 8
+   6 5
-------
```

Name: _____ Date: _____

Exercise 17 Addition - Expanded Version

1
```
     2 4 1
  +  2 5 3
  ─────────
         4
       9 0
     4 0 0
  ─────────
     4 9 4
  ─────────
```

2
```
     7 4 6
  +  1 3 2
  ─────────


  ─────────

  ─────────
```

3
```
     2 5 1
  +  3 1 4
  ─────────


  ─────────

  ─────────
```

4
```
     6 4 2
  +  3 1 7
  ─────────


  ─────────

  ─────────
```

5
```
     4 6 2
  +  2 2 5
  ─────────


  ─────────

  ─────────
```

6
```
     1 8 7
  +  5 1 0
  ─────────


  ─────────

  ─────────
```

7
```
     3 1 2
  +  3 4 5
  ─────────


  ─────────

  ─────────
```

8
```
     7 8 2
  +  2 1 6
  ─────────


  ─────────

  ─────────
```

9
```
     5 6 2
  +  3 2 7
  ─────────


  ─────────

  ─────────
```

10
```
     2 3 8
  +  6 1 1
  ─────────


  ─────────

  ─────────
```

11
```
     1 7 3
  +  8 2 6
  ─────────


  ─────────

  ─────────
```

12
```
     5 0 6
  +  2 5 3
  ─────────


  ─────────

  ─────────
```

Name:_____ Date:_____

Exercise 18 Addition - Expanded Version

1

```
      2 3 7
  +   4 1 8
  ──────────
        1 5
        4 0
      6 0 0
  ──────────
      6 5 5
  ──────────
```

2

```
      6 2 5
  +   1 3 6
  ──────────

  ──────────
```

3

```
      7 2 6
  +   1 5 8
  ──────────

  ──────────
```

4

```
      1 3 2
  +   5 6 8
  ──────────

  ──────────
```

5

```
      4 2 7
  +   3 5 5
  ──────────
```

6

```
      6 7 2
  +   2 1 8
  ──────────
```

7

```
      5 5 6
  +   2 0 8
  ──────────
```

8

```
      3 2 4
  +   5 3 7
  ──────────
```

9

```
      8 4 9
  +   1 3 7
  ──────────
```

10

```
      6 5 2
  +   2 4 8
  ──────────
```

11

```
      3 2 7
  +   2 3 8
  ──────────
```

12

```
      4 2 9
  +   3 6 4
  ──────────
```

Name: _____ Date: _____

Exercise 19 Addition - Expanded Version

1
```
    4 7 1
 +  3 9 3
 _____
        4
    1 6 0
    7 0 0
 _____
    8 6 4
 _____
```

2
```
    4 5 2
 +  3 6 3
 _____

 _____
```

3
```
    2 1 8
 +  3 9 1
 _____

 _____
```

4
```
    3 7 3
 +  4 3 1
 _____

 _____
```

5
```
    7 2 7
 +  1 9 2
```

6
```
    2 4 6
 +  3 7 2
```

7
```
    4 8 9
 +  2 4 0
```

8
```
    7 8 2
 +  1 5 3
```

9
```
    4 8 3
 +  2 4 6
```

10
```
    3 7 4
 +  2 4 3
```

11
```
    5 8 1
 +  3 4 6
```

12
```
    3 2 6
 +  5 9 2
```

Name:_____ Date:_____

Exercise 20 Addition - Expanded Version

1
```
    4 8 7
+   3 7 8
─────────
      1 5
    1 5 0
    7 0 0
─────────
    8 6 5
─────────
```

2
```
    3 2 9
+   1 7 8
─────────

─────────

─────────
```

3
```
    6 4 5
+   2 7 8
─────────

─────────

─────────
```

4
```
    3 1 2
+   4 9 9
─────────

─────────

─────────
```

5
```
    5 6 4
+   3 6 8
─────────

─────────

─────────
```

6
```
    2 4 4
+   3 7 6
─────────

─────────

─────────
```

7
```
    6 4 2
+   2 8 9
─────────

─────────

─────────
```

8
```
    2 8 7
+   1 4 5
─────────

─────────

─────────
```

9
```
    3 6 1
+   2 8 9
─────────

─────────

─────────
```

10
```
    6 7 4
+   2 4 8
─────────

─────────

─────────
```

11
```
    3 4 8
+   3 9 3
─────────

─────────

─────────
```

12
```
    5 7 3
+   3 4 8
─────────

─────────

─────────
```

Exercise 21 Addition - Expanded Version

1
```
    7 4 1
+   6 2 2
        3
      6 0
  1 3 0 0
─────────
  1 3 6 3
```

2
```
    4 5 2
+   7 3 4
─────────

─────────
```

3
```
    8 1 5
+   6 5 4
─────────

─────────
```

4
```
    5 1 4
+   6 3 2
─────────

─────────
```

5
```
    4 6 3
+   7 3 2
─────────

─────────
```

6
```
    7 4 8
+   5 2 0
─────────

─────────
```

7
```
    6 4 4
+   4 2 3
─────────

─────────
```

8
```
    3 4 8
+   8 3 1
─────────

─────────
```

9
```
    7 6 4
+   8 2 3
─────────

─────────
```

10
```
    5 7 3
+   7 2 5
─────────

─────────
```

11
```
    6 4 1
+   8 0 7
─────────

─────────
```

12
```
    2 4 7
+   9 2 2
─────────

─────────
```

Name:_____ Date:_____

Exercise 22 Addition - Expanded Version

1
```
    7 2 7
+   9 4 9
─────────
      1 6
      6 0
  1 6 0 0
─────────
  1 6 7 6
```

2
```
    4 1 4
+   6 7 6
─────────

─────────
```

3
```
    7 0 9
+   4 9 5
─────────

─────────
```

4
```
    6 3 8
+   5 5 8
─────────

─────────
```

5
```
    2 6 4
+   8 2 8
─────────

─────────
```

6
```
    8 5 8
+   6 2 5
─────────

─────────
```

7
```
    4 2 7
+   8 3 8
─────────

─────────
```

8
```
    7 4 3
+   6 0 8
─────────

─────────
```

9
```
    2 1 7
+   9 8 5
─────────

─────────
```

10
```
    3 2 6
+   7 3 7
─────────

─────────
```

11
```
    2 4 5
+   9 3 6
─────────

─────────
```

12
```
    2 3 7
+   8 2 6
─────────

─────────
```

Name:_____ Date:_____

Exercise 23 Addition - Expanded Version

1

```
    7 8 1
+   8 7 2
    ___
        3
    1 5 0
  1 5 0 0
  _____
  1 6 5 3
  _____
```

2

```
    6 4 1
+   5 8 2
  _____

  _____
```

3

```
    3 9 4
+   8 2 1
  _____

  _____
```

4

```
    6 3 1
+   7 8 5
  _____

  _____
```

5

```
    9 7 2
+   4 6 7
  _____

  _____
```

6

```
    2 8 3
+   9 7 5
  _____

  _____
```

7

```
    3 4 5
+   8 7 2
  _____

  _____
```

8

```
    6 1 8
+   5 9 1
  _____

  _____
```

9

```
    7 2 9
+   6 9 0
  _____

  _____
```

10

```
    5 1 3
+   8 9 2
  _____

  _____
```

11

```
    6 7 2
+   8 4 5
  _____

  _____
```

12

```
    4 8 8
+   9 6 1
  _____

  _____
```

Name:_____ Date: _____

Exercise 24 Addition - Expanded Version

1
```
    7 8 7
+   9 6 5
_____
    1 2
    1 4 0
  1 6 0 0
_____
  1 7 5 2
```

2
```
    8 2 5
+   7 9 8
_____

_____
```

3
```
    4 6 3
+   7 8 9
_____

_____
```

4
```
    5 7 4
+   9 4 8
_____

_____
```

5
```
    6 7 3
+   5 4 8
_____

_____
```

6
```
    6 4 5
+   7 8 9
_____

_____
```

7
```
    3 2 7
+   8 9 6
_____

_____
```

8
```
    5 5 5
+   7 6 8
_____

_____
```

9
```
    3 2 8
+   8 9 4
_____

_____
```

10
```
    2 8 5
+   9 3 7
_____

_____
```

11
```
    7 4 8
+   3 9 3
_____

_____
```

12
```
    8 4 7
+   6 7 8
_____

_____
```

Name:_____ Date:_____

Exercise 25 Subtraction - Basic Mental Methods

1 30 - 24 = [6]   **9** 90 - 82 = [ ]

2 80 - 72 = [ ]   **10** 40 - 32 = [ ]

3 40 - 38 = [ ]   **11** 50 - 41 = [ ]

4 30 - 26 = [ ]   **12** 30 - 22 = [ ]

5 50 - 44 = [ ]   **13** 70 - 63 = [ ]

6 80 - 78 = [ ]   **14** 80 - 74 = [ ]

7 40 - 36 = [ ]   **15** 90 - 86 = [ ]

8 70 - 64 = [ ]   **16** 40 - 38 = [ ]

Exercise 26   Subtraction - Basic Mental Methods

1 7 - 2 = [5]   so   700 - 200 = [500]

2 9 - 4 = [ ]   so   900 - 400 = [ ]

3 8 - 2 = [ ]   so   800 - 200 = [ ]

4 6 - 4 = [ ]   so   600 - 400 = [ ]

5 7 - 4 = [ ]   so   700 - 400 = [ ]

6 4 - 1 = [ ]   so   400 - 100 = [ ]

7 8 - 5 = [ ]   so   800 - 500 = [ ]

8 5 - 3 = [ ]   so   500 - 300 = [ ]

9 7 - 5 = [ ]   so   700 - 500 = [ ]

10 4 - 2 = [ ]   so   400 - 200 = [ ]

Name: _____ Date: _____

Exercise 27 Subtraction - Basic Mental Methods

1. $8 - 1 =$ [7] so $80 - 10 =$ [70]
2. $7 - 5 =$ [　] so $70 - 50 =$ [　]
3. $8 - 3 =$ [　] so $80 - 30 =$ [　]
4. $9 - 4 =$ [　] so $90 - 40 =$ [　]
5. $5 - 2 =$ [　] so $50 - 20 =$ [　]
6. $4 - 1 =$ [　] so $40 - 10 =$ [　]
7. $8 - 4 =$ [　] so $80 - 40 =$ [　]
8. $6 - 4 =$ [　] so $60 - 40 =$ [　]
9. $7 - 3 =$ [　] so $70 - 30 =$ [　]
10. $4 - 2 =$ [　] so $40 - 20 =$ [　]
11. $8 - 5 =$ [　] so $80 - 50 =$ [　]

Exercise 28 Subtraction - Basic Mental Methods

1. $14 - 8 =$ [6] so $140 - 80 =$ [60]
2. $13 - 9 =$ [　] so $130 - 90 =$ [　]
3. $13 - 5 =$ [　] so $130 - 50 =$ [　]
4. $14 - 7 =$ [　] so $140 - 70 =$ [　]
5. $11 - 8 =$ [　] so $110 - 80 =$ [　]
6. $13 - 6 =$ [　] so $130 - 60 =$ [　]
7. $12 - 5 =$ [　] so $120 - 50 =$ [　]
8. $10 - 7 =$ [　] so $100 - 70 =$ [　]
9. $15 - 8 =$ [　] so $150 - 80 =$ [　]
10. $16 - 9 =$ [　] so $160 - 90 =$ [　]
11. $11 - 4 =$ [　] so $110 - 40 =$ [　]

Name:_____ Date:_____

Exercise 29
Subtraction - Jumping Method

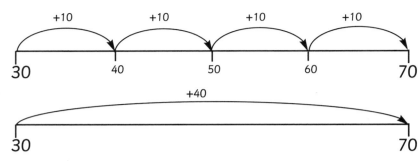

1 70 - 30 = | 40 | or

---

2 60 - 40 = | | 40 _____ 60

3 80 - 30 = | | 30 _____ 80

4 90 - 40 = | | 40 _____ 90

5 60 - 20 = | | 20 _____ 60

6 80 - 50 = | | 50 _____ 80

7 90 - 20 = | | 20 _____ 90

8 50 - 30 = | | 30 ___+10___+10___+10___+10___ 50

Name:_____ Date:_____

Exercise 30
Subtraction - Jumping Method

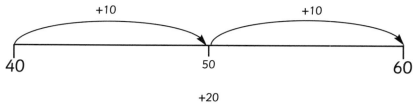

1 60 - 40 = | 20 | or

2 80 - 30 = | |

3 70 - 20 = | |

4 50 - 30 = | |

5 80 - 20 = | |

6 90 - 50 = | |

7 70 - 30 = | |

Name: _____ Date: _____

Exercise 31
Subtraction - Jumping Method

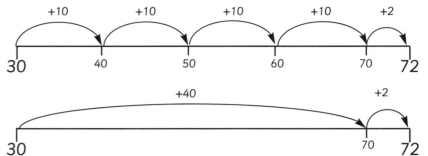

1 72 - 30 = | 42 | or

2 86 - 50 = [ ]

50 ⌐—————————————————————————⌐ 86

3 57 - 20 = [ ]

20 ⌐—————————————————————————⌐ 57

4 69 - 40 = [ ]

40 ⌐—————————————————————————⌐ 69

5 78 - 40 = [ ]

40 ⌐—————————————————————————⌐ 78

6 96 - 50 = [ ]

50 ⌐—————————————————————————⌐ 96

7 58 - 30 = [ ]

30 ⌐—————————————————————————⌐ 58

Name: _____ Date: _____

Exercise 32
Subtraction - Jumping Method

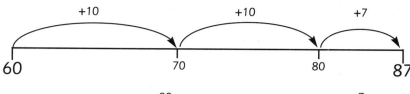

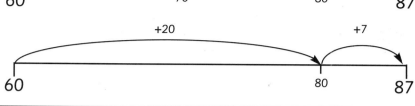

1 87 - 60 = | 27 | or

---

2 57 - 30 = | |

3 84 - 50 = | |

4 97 - 60 = | |

5 63 - 40 = | |

6 89 - 20 = | |

7 73 - 40 = | |

Name: _____ Date: _____

Exercise 33
Subtraction - Jumping Method

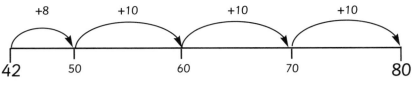

1 80 - 42 = $\boxed{38}$ or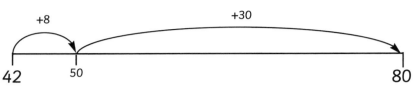

---

2 70 - 38 = $\boxed{}$

38 ⌐_____⌐ 70

3 40 - 27 = $\boxed{}$

27 ⌐_____⌐ 40

4 80 - 46 = $\boxed{}$

46 ⌐_____⌐ 80

5 60 - 28 = $\boxed{}$

28 ⌐_____⌐ 60

6 90 - 63 = $\boxed{}$

63 ⌐_____⌐ 90

7 50 - 34 = $\boxed{}$

34 ⌐_____⌐ 50

Name:_____ Date:_____

Exercise 34
Subtraction - Jumping Method

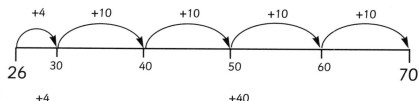

1 70 - 26 = [44] or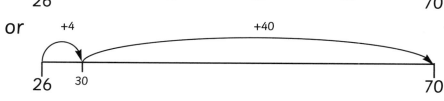

---

2 80 - 27 = [   ]

3 50 - 23 = [   ]

4 60 - 43 = [   ]

5 90 - 50 = [   ]

6 80 - 24 = [   ]

7 70 - 22 = [   ]

Name:_____ Date:_____

Exercise 35
Subtraction - Jumping Method

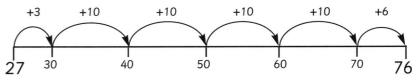

1 76 - 27 = | 49 | or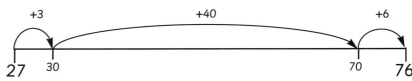

---

2 55 - 36 = [ ]

```
36 _____ 55
```

3 82 - 38 = [ ]

```
38 _____ 82
```

4 74 - 26 = [ ]

```
26 _____ 74
```

5 63 - 44 = [ ]

```
44 _____ 63
```

6 92 - 64 = [ ]

```
64 _____ 92
```

7 42 - 25 = [ ]

```
25 _____ 42
```

Name:_____ Date:_____

Exercise 36
Subtraction - Jumping Method

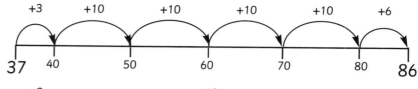

1   86 - 37   = | 49 | or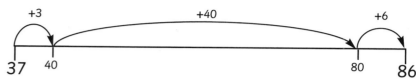

---

2   94 - 26   =   [ ]

3   72 - 46   =   [ ]

4   83 - 26   =   [ ]

5   46 - 28   =   [ ]

6   63 - 47   =   [ ]

7   91 - 64   =   [ ]

Name:_____ Date:_____

Exercise 37 Subtraction - Jumping Method

1 700 - 461 = | 239 |

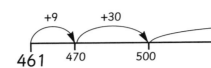

---

2 300 - 197 = | |

3 500 - 284 = | |

4 400 - 236 = | |

5 600 - 349 = | |

6 300 - 217 = | |

7 500 - 360 = | |

Name:_____ Date:_____

Exercise 38 Subtraction - Jumping Method

1 408 - 297 = ☐ 111 ☐

$+3$ $+100$ $+8$

297 300   400   408

---

2 606 - 498 = ☐

3 405 - 326 = ☐

4 508 - 392 = ☐

5 307 - 194 = ☐

6 603 - 487 = ☐

7 508 - 436 = ☐

Name:_____ Date:_____

Exercise 39 Subtraction - Jumping Method

1 562 - 348 = [214]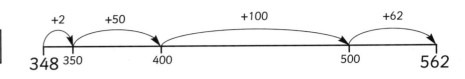

---

2 326 - 178 = [ ]

3 487 - 284 = [ ]

4 339 - 218 = [ ]

5 486 - 324 = [ ]

6 584 - 452 = [ ]

7 347 - 156 = [ ]

Name:_____ Date:_____

Exercise 40 Subtraction - Jumping Method

1 364 - 286 = | 78 |

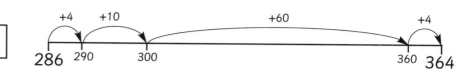

---

2 412 - 246 = | |

3 552 - 374 = | |

4 294 - 160 = | |

5 527 - 368 = | |

6 371 - 256 = | |

7 536 - 417 = | |

Exercise 41 Subtraction - Jumping Method

1 3002 - 2984 = $\boxed{18}$

```
        +6            +10         +2
2984        2990              3000  3002
```

---

2 4007 - 3994 = $\boxed{}$

3 4003 - 3992 = $\boxed{}$

4 2009 - 1986 = $\boxed{}$

5 4005 - 3993 = $\boxed{}$

6 6002 - 5991 = $\boxed{}$

7 3001 - 2983 = $\boxed{}$

Name:_____ Date:_____

Exercise 42 Subtraction - Jumping Method

1 3012 - 2996 = [16]

```
        +4              +12
    ⌢              ⌢
2996      3000                    3012
```

---

2 4019 - 3996 = [   ] ⌐_____⌐

3 2016 - 1989 = [   ] ⌐_____⌐

4 5019 - 4995 = [   ] ⌐_____⌐

5 3015 - 2981 = [   ] ⌐_____⌐

6 4017 - 3992 = [   ] ⌐_____⌐

7 6013 - 5988 = [   ] ⌐_____⌐

Name:_____ Date:_____

Exercise 43 Subtraction - Jumping Method

1 5.7 - 4.3 = $\boxed{1.4}$

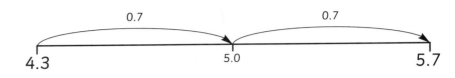

---

2 6.3 - 5.7 = ☐

3 5.8 - 3.8 = ☐

4 7.6 - 5.2 = ☐

5 4.5 - 3.6 = ☐

6 8.9 - 7.0 = ☐

7 2.4 - 1.8 = ☐

Name:_____ Date:_____

Exercise 44 Subtraction - Jumping Method

1 25.6 - 18.7 = [6.9]

+0.3   +6.0   +0.6

18.7   19.0   25.0   25.6

---

2 22.4 - 17.8 = [ ]

3 32.8 - 25.6 = [ ]

4 18.7 - 13.5 = [ ]

5 28.2 - 15.6 = [ ]

6 36.3 - 28.9 = [ ]

7 56.7 - 43.8 = [ ]

Name: _____   Date: _____

Exercise 45 Subtraction - Expanded Version

1 563-241= [322]

$$\begin{array}{r} 500+60+3 \\ - \quad 200+40+1 \\ \hline 300+20+2 \end{array}$$

2 745-324= [   ]

$$\begin{array}{r} 700+40+5 \\ - \quad 300+20+4 \\ \hline + \qquad + \end{array}$$

3 678-455= [   ]

$$\begin{array}{r} 600+70+8 \\ - \quad 400+50+5 \\ \hline + \qquad + \end{array}$$

4 481-370= [   ]

$$\begin{array}{r} 400+80+1 \\ - \quad 300+70+0 \\ \hline + \qquad + \end{array}$$

5 296-143= [   ]

$$\begin{array}{r} 200+90+6 \\ - \quad 100+40+3 \\ \hline + \qquad + \end{array}$$

6 254-123= [   ]

$$\begin{array}{r} 200+50+4 \\ - \quad 100+20+3 \\ \hline + \qquad + \end{array}$$

7 726-413= [   ]

$$\begin{array}{r} 700+20+6 \\ - \quad 400+10+3 \\ \hline + \qquad + \end{array}$$

8 894-623= [   ]

$$\begin{array}{r} 800+90+4 \\ - \quad 600+20+3 \\ \hline + \qquad + \end{array}$$

9 879-412= [   ]

$$\begin{array}{r} 800+70+9 \\ - \quad 400+10+2 \\ \hline + \qquad + \end{array}$$

10 685-421= [   ]

$$\begin{array}{r} 600+80+5 \\ - \quad 400+20+1 \\ \hline + \qquad + \end{array}$$

11 877-241= [   ]

$$\begin{array}{r} 800+70+7 \\ - \quad 200+40+1 \\ \hline + \qquad + \end{array}$$

12 894-230= [   ]

$$\begin{array}{r} 800+90+4 \\ - \quad 200+30+0 \\ \hline + \qquad + \end{array}$$

Name:_____   Date:_____

Exercise 46 Subtraction - Expanded Version

1
474-123= [351]

$$\begin{array}{r} 400+70+4 \\ -\ \underline{100+20+3} \\ \underline{300+50+1} \end{array}$$

2
736-422= [ ]

$$\begin{array}{r} +\quad+ \\ -\ \underline{+\quad+} \\ \underline{+\quad+} \end{array}$$

3
598-426= [ ]

$$\begin{array}{r} +\quad+ \\ -\ \underline{+\quad+} \\ \underline{+\quad+} \end{array}$$

4
937-615= [ ]

$$\begin{array}{r} +\quad+ \\ -\ \underline{+\quad+} \\ \underline{+\quad+} \end{array}$$

5
682-331= [ ]

$$\begin{array}{r} +\quad+ \\ -\ \underline{+\quad+} \\ \underline{+\quad+} \end{array}$$

6
875-532= [ ]

$$\begin{array}{r} +\quad+ \\ -\ \underline{+\quad+} \\ \underline{+\quad+} \end{array}$$

7
376-146= [ ]

$$\begin{array}{r} +\quad+ \\ -\ \underline{+\quad+} \\ \underline{+\quad+} \end{array}$$

8
847-635= [ ]

$$\begin{array}{r} +\quad+ \\ -\ \underline{+\quad+} \\ \underline{+\quad+} \end{array}$$

9
248-136= [ ]

$$\begin{array}{r} +\quad+ \\ -\ \underline{+\quad+} \\ \underline{+\quad+} \end{array}$$

10
758-545= [ ]

$$\begin{array}{r} +\quad+ \\ -\ \underline{+\quad+} \\ \underline{+\quad+} \end{array}$$

11
659-338= [ ]

$$\begin{array}{r} +\quad+ \\ -\ \underline{+\quad+} \\ \underline{+\quad+} \end{array}$$

12
426-115= [ ]

$$\begin{array}{r} +\quad+ \\ -\ \underline{+\quad+} \\ \underline{+\quad+} \end{array}$$

Name:_____ Date:_____

Exercise 47 Subtraction - Expanded Version

1
671-246= [425]

$$\begin{array}{r} 601 \\ 600+\cancel{70}+1 \\ -\ 200+40+6 \\ \hline 400+20+5 \end{array}$$

2
583-355= [ ]

$$\begin{array}{r} 500+80+3 \\ -\ 300+50+5 \\ \hline ++ \end{array}$$

3
758-429= [ ]

$$\begin{array}{r} 700+50+8 \\ -\ 400+20+9 \\ \hline ++ \end{array}$$

4
384-258= [ ]

$$\begin{array}{r} 300+80+4 \\ -\ 200+50+8 \\ \hline ++ \end{array}$$

5
490-265= [ ]

$$\begin{array}{r} 400+90+0 \\ -\ 200+60+5 \\ \hline ++ \end{array}$$

6
685-436= [ ]

$$\begin{array}{r} 600+80+5 \\ -\ 400+30+6 \\ \hline ++ \end{array}$$

7
892-648= [ ]

$$\begin{array}{r} 800+90+2 \\ -\ 600+40+8 \\ \hline ++ \end{array}$$

8
978-539= [ ]

$$\begin{array}{r} 900+70+8 \\ -\ 500+30+9 \\ \hline ++ \end{array}$$

9
283-158= [ ]

$$\begin{array}{r} 200+80+3 \\ -\ 100+50+8 \\ \hline ++ \end{array}$$

10
471-236= [ ]

$$\begin{array}{r} 400+70+1 \\ -\ 200+30+6 \\ \hline ++ \end{array}$$

11
544-218= [ ]

$$\begin{array}{r} 500+40+4 \\ -\ 200+10+8 \\ \hline ++ \end{array}$$

12
733-514= [ ]

$$\begin{array}{r} 700+30+3 \\ -\ 500+10+4 \\ \hline ++ \end{array}$$

Name:_____   Date:_____

Exercise 48 Subtraction - Expanded Version

1 791-476= | 315 |

$$\begin{array}{r} \overset{80\ \ \ 1}{700+\cancel{90}+1} \\ -\ \ \ 400+70+6 \\ \hline 300+10+5 \end{array}$$

2 655-327= | |

$$\begin{array}{r} +\ \ +\ \ \\ -\ \ +\ \ +\ \ \\ \hline +\ \ +\ \ \end{array}$$

3 248-119= | |

$$\begin{array}{r} +\ \ +\ \ \\ -\ \ +\ \ +\ \ \\ \hline +\ \ +\ \ \end{array}$$

4 574-346= | |

$$\begin{array}{r} +\ \ +\ \ \\ -\ \ +\ \ +\ \ \\ \hline +\ \ +\ \ \end{array}$$

5 983-725= | |

$$\begin{array}{r} +\ \ +\ \ \\ -\ \ +\ \ +\ \ \\ \hline +\ \ +\ \ \end{array}$$

6 437-218= | |

$$\begin{array}{r} +\ \ +\ \ \\ -\ \ +\ \ +\ \ \\ \hline +\ \ +\ \ \end{array}$$

7 965-627= | |

$$\begin{array}{r} +\ \ +\ \ \\ -\ \ +\ \ +\ \ \\ \hline +\ \ +\ \ \end{array}$$

8 336-117= | |

$$\begin{array}{r} +\ \ +\ \ \\ -\ \ +\ \ +\ \ \\ \hline +\ \ +\ \ \end{array}$$

9 634-525= | |

$$\begin{array}{r} +\ \ +\ \ \\ -\ \ +\ \ +\ \ \\ \hline +\ \ +\ \ \end{array}$$

10 263-148= | |

$$\begin{array}{r} +\ \ +\ \ \\ -\ \ +\ \ +\ \ \\ \hline +\ \ +\ \ \end{array}$$

11 345-126= | |

$$\begin{array}{r} +\ \ +\ \ \\ -\ \ +\ \ +\ \ \\ \hline +\ \ +\ \ \end{array}$$

12 784-519= | |

$$\begin{array}{r} +\ \ +\ \ \\ -\ \ +\ \ +\ \ \\ \hline +\ \ +\ \ \end{array}$$

Name: _____ Date: _____

Exercise 49 Subtraction - Expanded Version

1 917-384= [533]

$$\begin{array}{r} 800 \quad 1 \\ \cancel{900}+10+7 \\ -\ 300+80+4 \\ \hline 500+30+3 \end{array}$$

2 876-483= [ ]

$$\begin{array}{r} 800+70+6 \\ -\ 400+80+3 \\ \hline +\qquad + \end{array}$$

3 252-161= [ ]

$$\begin{array}{r} 200+50+2 \\ -\ 100+60+1 \\ \hline +\qquad + \end{array}$$

4 346-184= [ ]

$$\begin{array}{r} 300+40+6 \\ -\ 100+80+4 \\ \hline +\qquad + \end{array}$$

5 243-192= [ ]

$$\begin{array}{r} 200+40+3 \\ -\ 100+90+2 \\ \hline +\qquad + \end{array}$$

6 618-335= [ ]

$$\begin{array}{r} 600+10+8 \\ -\ 300+30+5 \\ \hline +\qquad + \end{array}$$

7 428-230= [ ]

$$\begin{array}{r} 400+20+8 \\ -\ 200+30+0 \\ \hline +\qquad + \end{array}$$

8 571-381= [ ]

$$\begin{array}{r} 500+70+1 \\ -\ 300+80+1 \\ \hline +\qquad + \end{array}$$

9 932-751= [ ]

$$\begin{array}{r} 900+30+2 \\ -\ 700+50+1 \\ \hline +\qquad + \end{array}$$

10 659-283= [ ]

$$\begin{array}{r} 600+50+9 \\ -\ 200+80+3 \\ \hline +\qquad + \end{array}$$

11 385-194= [ ]

$$\begin{array}{r} 300+80+5 \\ -\ 100+90+4 \\ \hline +\qquad + \end{array}$$

12 417-284= [ ]

$$\begin{array}{r} 400+10+7 \\ -\ 200+80+4 \\ \hline +\qquad + \end{array}$$

Name:_____   Date:_____

Exercise 50 Subtraction - Expanded Version

1 814-392= [422]

```
700      1
8̶0̶0̶    +10   +4
-300    +90   +2
 400    +20   +2
```

2 528-386= [ ]

```
        +     +
-       +     +
        +     +
```

3 335-164= [ ]

```
        +     +
-       +     +
        +     +
```

4 438-176= [ ]

```
        +     +
-       +     +
        +     +
```

5 953-762= [ ]

```
        +     +
-       +     +
        +     +
```

6 639-417= [ ]

```
        +     +
-       +     +
        +     +
```

7 218-135= [ ]

```
        +     +
-       +     +
        +     +
```

8 687-391= [ ]

```
        +     +
-       +     +
        +     +
```

9 546-284= [ ]

```
        +     +
-       +     +
        +     +
```

10 739-475= [ ]

```
        +     +
-       +     +
        +     +
```

11 214-182= [ ]

```
        +     +
-       +     +
        +     +
```

12 865-592= [ ]

```
        +     +
-       +     +
        +     +
```

Name:_____   Date:_____

Exercise 51 Subtraction - Expanded Version

1 724-697= [27]

$$\begin{array}{r} 600\ \ 110\ \ 1 \\ \cancel{700}+\cancel{20}+4 \\ -\ \ 600+90+7 \\ \hline 0+20+7 \end{array}$$

2 913-645= [   ]

$$\begin{array}{r} 900+10+3 \\ -\ 600+40+5 \\ \hline +\ \ \ \ \ + \end{array}$$

3 241-152= [   ]

$$\begin{array}{r} 200+40+1 \\ -\ 100+50+2 \\ \hline +\ \ \ \ \ + \end{array}$$

4 364-185= [   ]

$$\begin{array}{r} 300+60+4 \\ -\ 100+80+5 \\ \hline +\ \ \ \ \ + \end{array}$$

5 762-593= [   ]

$$\begin{array}{r} 700+60+2 \\ -\ 500+90+3 \\ \hline +\ \ \ \ \ + \end{array}$$

6 874-685= [   ]

$$\begin{array}{r} 800+70+4 \\ -\ 600+80+5 \\ \hline +\ \ \ \ \ + \end{array}$$

7 551-385= [   ]

$$\begin{array}{r} 500+50+1 \\ -\ 300+80+5 \\ \hline +\ \ \ \ \ + \end{array}$$

8 632-348= [   ]

$$\begin{array}{r} 600+30+2 \\ -\ 300+40+8 \\ \hline +\ \ \ \ \ + \end{array}$$

9 442-263= [   ]

$$\begin{array}{r} 400+40+2 \\ -\ 200+60+3 \\ \hline +\ \ \ \ \ + \end{array}$$

10 372-184= [   ]

$$\begin{array}{r} 300+70+2 \\ -\ 100+80+4 \\ \hline +\ \ \ \ \ + \end{array}$$

11 243-165= [   ]

$$\begin{array}{r} 200+40+3 \\ -\ 100+60+5 \\ \hline +\ \ \ \ \ + \end{array}$$

12 734-578= [   ]

$$\begin{array}{r} 700+30+4 \\ -\ 500+70+8 \\ \hline +\ \ \ \ \ + \end{array}$$

Name:_____   Date:_____

Exercise 52 Subtraction - Expanded Version

1 646-379= [267]

$$
\begin{array}{r}
\ \ \ 500\ \ \ 130\ \ 1 \\
\ \ \ \cancel{600}+\cancel{40}+6 \\
-\ \ \ 300+70+9 \\
\hline
200+60+7
\end{array}
$$

2 334-169= [   ]

$$
\begin{array}{r}
+\ \ \ \ \ + \\
-\ \ \ +\ \ \ \ \ + \\
\hline
+\ \ \ \ \ +
\end{array}
$$

3 544-267= [   ]

$$
\begin{array}{r}
+\ \ \ \ \ + \\
-\ \ \ +\ \ \ \ \ + \\
\hline
+\ \ \ \ \ +
\end{array}
$$

4 981-793= [   ]

$$
\begin{array}{r}
+\ \ \ \ \ + \\
-\ \ \ +\ \ \ \ \ + \\
\hline
+\ \ \ \ \ +
\end{array}
$$

5 427-248= [   ]

$$
\begin{array}{r}
+\ \ \ \ \ + \\
-\ \ \ +\ \ \ \ \ + \\
\hline
+\ \ \ \ \ +
\end{array}
$$

6 732-456= [   ]

$$
\begin{array}{r}
+\ \ \ \ \ + \\
-\ \ \ +\ \ \ \ \ + \\
\hline
+\ \ \ \ \ +
\end{array}
$$

7 650-278= [   ]

$$
\begin{array}{r}
+\ \ \ \ \ + \\
-\ \ \ +\ \ \ \ \ + \\
\hline
+\ \ \ \ \ +
\end{array}
$$

8 827-649= [   ]

$$
\begin{array}{r}
+\ \ \ \ \ + \\
-\ \ \ +\ \ \ \ \ + \\
\hline
+\ \ \ \ \ +
\end{array}
$$

9 472-185= [   ]

$$
\begin{array}{r}
+\ \ \ \ \ + \\
-\ \ \ +\ \ \ \ \ + \\
\hline
+\ \ \ \ \ +
\end{array}
$$

10 345-186= [   ]

$$
\begin{array}{r}
+\ \ \ \ \ + \\
-\ \ \ +\ \ \ \ \ + \\
\hline
+\ \ \ \ \ +
\end{array}
$$

11 456-278= [   ]

$$
\begin{array}{r}
+\ \ \ \ \ + \\
-\ \ \ +\ \ \ \ \ + \\
\hline
+\ \ \ \ \ +
\end{array}
$$

12 934-558= [   ]

$$
\begin{array}{r}
+\ \ \ \ \ + \\
-\ \ \ +\ \ \ \ \ + \\
\hline
+\ \ \ \ \ +
\end{array}
$$

Name:_____ Date:_____

Exercise 53 Addition Practice (Set out in your book)

1. 57 + 21 = ☐
2. 72 + 23 = ☐
3. 84 + 12 = ☐
4. 53 + 41 = ☐
5. 71 + 24 = ☐
6. 36 + 49 = ☐
7. 54 + 27 = ☐
8. 28 + 56 = ☐
9. 29 + 60 = ☐
10. 43 + 39 = ☐

11. 72 + 96 = ☐
12. 83 + 46 = ☐
13. 36 + 78 = ☐
14. 43 + 89 = ☐
15. 65 + 86 = ☐
16. 241 + 253 = ☐
17. 601 + 382 = ☐
18. 187 + 512 = ☐
19. 173 + 825 = ☐
20. 251 + 316 = ☐

21. 237 + 419 = ☐
22. 625 + 146 = ☐
23. 481 + 394 = ☐
24. 373 + 491 = ☐
25. 489 + 397 = ☐
26. 647 + 295 = ☐
27. 896 + 748 = ☐
28. 748 + 921 = ☐
29. 832 + 795 = ☐
30. 926 + 473 = ☐

Exercise 54 Addition Practice (Set out in your book)

1. 35 + 23 = ☐
2. 64 + 44 = ☐
3. 28 + 31 = ☐
4. 57 + 32 = ☐
5. 45 + 52 = ☐
6. 82 + 18 = ☐
7. 53 + 28 = ☐
8. 44 + 37 = ☐
9. 51 + 49 = ☐
10. 28 + 35 = ☐

11. 42 + 65 = ☐
12. 39 + 63 = ☐
13. 14 + 97 = ☐
14. 72 + 35 = ☐
15. 36 + 88 = ☐
16. 64 + 27 = ☐
17. 321 + 252 = ☐
18. 145 + 323 = ☐
19. 264 + 423 = ☐
20. 681 + 214 = ☐

21. 423 + 279 = ☐
22. 645 + 326 = ☐
23. 391 + 479 = ☐
24. 556 + 478 = ☐
25. 859 + 662 = ☐
26. 748 + 637 = ☐
27. 984 + 450 = ☐
28. 217 + 986 = ☐
29. 349 + 782 = ☐
30. 584 + 936 = ☐

Name:_____ Date: _____

Exercise 55 Addition Practice (Set out in your book)

1 $82 + 16$ = ☐	**11** $64 + 86$ = ☐	**21** $247 + 228$ = ☐
2 $65 + 32$ = ☐	**12** $29 + 89$ = ☐	**22** $456 + 374$ = ☐
3 $27 + 41$ = ☐	**13** $41 + 78$ = ☐	**23** $281 + 419$ = ☐
4 $56 + 33$ = ☐	**14** $34 + 92$ = ☐	**24** $823 + 184$ = ☐
5 $25 + 44$ = ☐	**15** $28 + 76$ = ☐	**25** $645 + 265$ = ☐
6 $63 + 28$ = ☐	**16** $231 + 427$ = ☐	**26** $826 + 485$ = ☐
7 $46 + 35$ = ☐	**17** $816 + 183$ = ☐	**27** $324 + 785$ = ☐
8 $26 + 48$ = ☐	**18** $266 + 323$ = ☐	**28** $462 + 839$ = ☐
9 $38 + 26$ = ☐	**19** $460 + 325$ = ☐	**29** $926 + 346$ = ☐
10 $42 + 39$ = ☐	**20** $618 + 351$ = ☐	**30** $817 + 587$ = ☐

Exercise 56 Addition Practice (Set out in your book)

1 $61 + 32$ = ☐	**11** $36 + 77$ = ☐	**21** $625 + 248$ = ☐
2 $86 + 12$ = ☐	**12** $22 + 89$ = ☐	**22** $382 + 219$ = ☐
3 $52 + 27$ = ☐	**13** $38 + 56$ = ☐	**23** $436 + 348$ = ☐
4 $82 + 16$ = ☐	**14** $42 + 74$ = ☐	**24** $842 + 159$ = ☐
5 $37 + 42$ = ☐	**15** $65 + 68$ = ☐	**25** $586 + 457$ = ☐
6 $46 + 33$ = ☐	**16** $373 + 215$ = ☐	**26** $325 + 687$ = ☐
7 $72 + 28$ = ☐	**17** $182 + 235$ = ☐	**27** $857 + 343$ = ☐
8 $45 + 36$ = ☐	**18** $581 + 317$ = ☐	**28** $739 + 580$ = ☐
9 $54 + 27$ = ☐	**19** $426 + 523$ = ☐	**29** $435 + 827$ = ☐
10 $28 + 64$ = ☐	**20** $382 + 116$ = ☐	**30** $243 + 798$ = ☐

Name:_____ Date:_____

Exercise 57 Addition Practice (Set out in your book)

1   $38 + 21$ = ☐   11 $64 + 38$ = ☐   21 $684 + 328$ = ☐

2   $24 + 73$ = ☐   12 $27 + 86$ = ☐   22 $256 + 784$ = ☐

3   $35 + 43$ = ☐   13 $42 + 69$ = ☐   23 $429 + 598$ = ☐

4   $52 + 43$ = ☐   14 $37 + 92$ = ☐   24 $371 + 853$ = ☐

5   $28 + 31$ = ☐   15 $85 + 46$ = ☐   25 $642 + 558$ = ☐

6   $42 + 35$ = ☐   16 $328 + 261$ = ☐   26 $428 + 760$ = ☐

7   $28 + 64$ = ☐   17 $564 + 232$ = ☐   27 $814 + 365$ = ☐

8   $72 + 19$ = ☐   18 $318 + 621$ = ☐   28 $764 + 658$ = ☐

9   $44 + 38$ = ☐   19 $542 + 336$ = ☐   29 $462 + 739$ = ☐

10 $26 + 45$ = ☐   20 $178 + 411$ = ☐   30 $512 + 864$ = ☐

Exercise 58 Addition Practice (Set out in your book)

1   $46 + 33$ = ☐   11 $54 + 47$ = ☐   21 $398 + 611$ = ☐

2   $27 + 32$ = ☐   12 $32 + 86$ = ☐   22 $247 + 328$ = ☐

3   $72 + 24$ = ☐   13 $27 + 75$ = ☐   23 $648 + 227$ = ☐

4   $38 + 21$ = ☐   14 $46 + 59$ = ☐   24 $548 + 737$ = ☐

5   $65 + 24$ = ☐   15 $54 + 67$ = ☐   25 $6.4 + 3.2$ = ☐

6   $27 + 72$ = ☐   16 $631 + 248$ = ☐   26 $5.6 + 2.0$ = ☐

7   $38 + 43$ = ☐   17 $712 + 253$ = ☐   27 $8.3 + 6.2$ = ☐

8   $55 + 36$ = ☐   18 $348 + 431$ = ☐   28 $5.6 + 3.5$ = ☐

9   $62 + 27$ = ☐   19 $552 + 324$ = ☐   29 $4.7 + 3.8$ = ☐

10 $32 + 49$ = ☐   20 $651 + 237$ = ☐   30 $2.6 + 4.3$ = ☐

Name: _____   Date: _____

Exercise 59 Addition Practice (Set out in your book)

1 34 + 22 = ☐   **11** 32 + 78 = ☐   **21** 347 + 234 = ☐

2 56 + 24 = ☐   **12** 56 + 48 = ☐   **22** 526 + 345 = ☐

3 25 + 32 = ☐   **13** 79 + 45 = ☐   **23** 243 + 328 = ☐

4 66 + 23 = ☐   **14** 63 + 82 = ☐   **24** 652 + 319 = ☐

5 42 + 37 = ☐   **15** 76 + 54 = ☐   **25** 436 + 528 = ☐

6 46 + 25 = ☐   **16** 614 + 325 = ☐   **26** 748 + 634 = ☐

7 27 + 38 = ☐   **17** 263 + 126 = ☐   **27** 2.78 + 8.23 = ☐

8 64 + 28 = ☐   **18** 472 + 314 = ☐   **28** 4.78 + 5.92 = ☐

9 34 + 20 = ☐   **19** 252 + 345 = ☐   **29** 3.18 + 8.92 = ☐

10 47 + 35 = ☐   **20** 348 + 231 = ☐   **30** 6.45 + 7.32 = ☐

Exercise 60 Addition Practice (Set out in your book)

1 65 + 24 = ☐   **11** 54 + 63 = ☐   **21** 345 + 236 = ☐

2 72 + 26 = ☐   **12** 72 + 34 = ☐   **22** 843 + 139 = ☐

3 45 + 32 = ☐   **13** 87 + 24 = ☐   **23** 644 + 237 = ☐

4 24 + 53 = ☐   **14** 48 + 52 = ☐   **24** 725 + 186 = ☐

5 17 + 42 = ☐   **15** 66 + 35 = ☐   **25** 632 + 348 = ☐

6 36 + 25 = ☐   **16** 652 + 206 = ☐   **26** 729 + 563 = ☐

7 63 + 28 = ☐   **17** 453 + 234 = ☐   **27** 6.24 + 3.91 = ☐

8 57 + 24 = ☐   **18** 173 + 214 = ☐   **28** 5.67 + 8.25 = ☐

9 39 + 52 = ☐   **19** 456 + 342 = ☐   **29** 3.76 + 7.53 = ☐

10 46 + 35 = ☐   **20** 184 + 413 = ☐   **30** 2.14 + 8.95 = ☐

Name:_____ Date:_____

Exercise 61 Subtraction Practice (Set out in your book)

1	90 - 40 = ☐	**11**	562 - 348 = ☐	**21**	5007 - 3994= ☐
2	60 - 20 = ☐	**12**	339 - 218 = ☐	**22**	3001 - 2983= ☐
3	69 - 40 = ☐	**13**	294 - 163 = ☐	**23**	3012 - 2996= ☐
4	96 - 50 = ☐	**14**	364 - 185 = ☐	**24**	3015 - 2981= ☐
5	70 - 38 = ☐	**15**	300 - 124 = ☐	**25**	6.3 - 5.7 = ☐
6	90 - 63 = ☐	**16**	871 - 283 = ☐	**26**	9.2 - 4.7 = ☐
7	74 - 26 = ☐	**17**	724 - 371 = ☐	**27**	8.6 - 2.1 = ☐
8	92 - 64 = ☐	**18**	621 - 481 = ☐	**28**	7.23 - 4.12 = ☐
9	700 - 241 = ☐	**19**	700 - 249 = ☐	**29**	8.91 - 7.14 = ☐
10	508 - 194 = ☐	**20**	816 - 317 = ☐	**30**	9.73 - 6.4 = ☐

Exercise 62 Subtraction Practice (Set out in your book)

1	60 - 30 = ☐	**11**	304 - 185 = ☐	**21**	2003 - 1987 = ☐
2	70 - 40 = ☐	**12**	834 - 265 = ☐	**22**	4002 - 3984 = ☐
3	86 - 50 = ☐	**13**	317 - 193 = ☐	**23**	5014 - 4995 = ☐
4	72 - 20 = ☐	**14**	691 - 462 = ☐	**24**	3009 - 2979 = ☐
5	50 - 36 = ☐	**15**	256 - 179 = ☐	**25**	8.6 - 2.4 = ☐
6	80 - 53 = ☐	**16**	725 - 248 = ☐	**26**	7.9 - 4.3 = ☐
7	64 - 37 = ☐	**17**	462 - 312 = ☐	**27**	2.4 - 1.7 = ☐
8	82 - 64 = ☐	**18**	948 - 765 = ☐	**28**	7.6 - 2.42 = ☐
9	94 - 48 = ☐	**19**	589 - 328 = ☐	**29**	9.4 - 7.61 = ☐
10	600 - 237 = ☐	**20**	673 - 564 = ☐	**30**	8.61 - 4.3 = ☐

Name: _____   Date: _____

Exercise 63 Subtraction Practice (Set out in your book)

1	80 - 30 = ☐	**11**	534 - 286 = ☐	**21**	8006 - 7994 = ☐
2	90 - 50 = ☐	**12**	348 - 279 = ☐	**22**	4002 - 2996 = ☐
3	73 - 50 = ☐	**13**	652 - 498 = ☐	**23**	5012 - 3992 = ☐
4	94 - 60 = ☐	**14**	473 - 349 = ☐	**24**	7015 - 5986 = ☐
5	80 - 52 = ☐	**15**	512 - 246 = ☐	**25**	7.4 - 3.9 = ☐
6	60 - 46 = ☐	**16**	843 - 526 = ☐	**26**	4.2 - 3.6 = ☐
7	38 - 29 = ☐	**17**	642 - 491 = ☐	**27**	9.5 - 3.9 = ☐
8	84 - 67 = ☐	**18**	376 - 238 = ☐	**28**	6.2 - 4.23 = ☐
9	500 - 326 = ☐	**19**	600 - 434 = ☐	**29**	8.4 - 7.54 = ☐
10	608 - 276 = ☐	**20**	716 - 565 = ☐	**30**	9.25 - 6.3 = ☐

Exercise 64 Subtraction Practice (Set out in your book)

1	70 - 30 = ☐	**11**	428 - 363 = ☐	**21**	6007 - 5992 = ☐
2	90 - 60 = ☐	**12**	357 - 248 = ☐	**22**	7003 - 6994 = ☐
3	68 - 40 = ☐	**13**	806 - 615 = ☐	**23**	5004 - 4986 = ☐
4	86 - 50 = ☐	**14**	235 - 187 = ☐	**24**	8018 - 7998 = ☐
5	90 - 48 = ☐	**15**	742 - 539 = ☐	**25**	8.6 - 2.7 = ☐
6	50 - 36 = ☐	**16**	593 - 364 = ☐	**26**	9.4 - 3.1 = ☐
7	75 - 48 = ☐	**17**	984 - 721 = ☐	**27**	7.3 - 4.9 = ☐
8	65 - 37 = ☐	**18**	672 - 493 = ☐	**28**	6.23 - 4.7 = ☐
9	84 - 49 = ☐	**19**	269 - 188 = ☐	**29**	8.93 - 2.07 = ☐
10	500 - 432 = ☐	**20**	433 - 329 = ☐	**30**	6.4 - 5.32 = ☐

Name:_____ Date: _____

Exercise 65 Subtraction Practice (Set out in your book)

1 50 - 30 = ☐   **11** 429 - 366 = ☐   **21** 6004 - 5988 = ☐

2 70 - 60 = ☐   **12** 991 - 724 = ☐   **22** 3009 - 2978 = ☐

3 66 - 40 = ☐   **13** 182 - 113 = ☐   **23** 5015 - 4992 = ☐

4 58 - 30 = ☐   **14** 837 - 728 = ☐   **24** 4012 - 3997 = ☐

5 90 - 67 = ☐   **15** 238 - 149 = ☐   **25** 8.6 - 5.9 = ☐

6 70 - 43 = ☐   **16** 563 - 328 = ☐   **26** 7.3 - 2.4 = ☐

7 76 - 55 = ☐   **17** 376 - 184 = ☐   **27** 6.6 - 2.9 = ☐

8 57 - 33 = ☐   **18** 745 - 527 = ☐   **28** 7.24 - 4.69 = ☐

9 500 - 338 = ☐   **19** 321 - 210 = ☐   **29** 8.41 - 3.97 = ☐

10 606 - 472 = ☐   **20** 654 - 528 = ☐   **30** 6.4 - 2.48 = ☐

Exercise 66 Subtraction Practice (Set out in your book)

1 80 - 60 = ☐   **11** 456 - 266 = ☐   **21** 2012 - 1981 = ☐

2 90 - 70 = ☐   **12** 165 - 119 = ☐   **22** 4019 - 3992 = ☐

3 42 - 30 = ☐   **13** 728 - 564 = ☐   **23** 3001 - 2996 = ☐

4 76 - 50 = ☐   **14** 243 - 185 = ☐   **24** 6007 - 5992 = ☐

5 50 - 39 = ☐   **15** 637 - 427 = ☐   **25** 6.4 - 3.4 = ☐

6 30 - 18 = ☐   **16** 339 - 284 = ☐   **26** 8.9 - 2.7 = ☐

7 86 - 65 = ☐   **17** 945 - 732 = ☐   **27** 7.9 - 2.8 = ☐

8 43 - 27 = ☐   **18** 576 - 435 = ☐   **28** 4.82 - 2.1 = ☐

9 600 - 438 = ☐   **19** 898 - 632 = ☐   **29** 7.4 - 2.86 = ☐

10 506 - 293 = ☐   **20** 287 - 148 = ☐   **30** 9.6 - 3.67 = ☐

Name:_____ **Date:**_____

Exercise 67 Subtraction Practice (Set out in your book)

1 60 - 40 = ☐	**11** 428 - 377 = ☐	**21** 3003 - 2998 = ☐
2 40 - 30 = ☐	**12** 946 - 742 = ☐	**22** 8014 - 7994 = ☐
3 89 - 40 = ☐	**13** 287 - 198 = ☐	**23** 5006 - 4992 = ☐
4 68 - 30 = ☐	**14** 834 - 554 = ☐	**24** 9020 - 8999 = ☐
5 80 - 37 = ☐	**15** 375 - 203 = ☐	**25** 7.4 - 2.9 = ☐
6 40 - 29 = ☐	**16** 732 - 519 = ☐	**26** 8.3 - 6.7 = ☐
7 56 - 35 = ☐	**17** 543 - 364 = ☐	**27** 4.8 - 2.9 = ☐
8 73 - 37 = ☐	**18** 691 - 428 = ☐	**28** 7.9 - 5.63 = ☐
9 300 - 238 = ☐	**19** 867 - 738 = ☐	**29** 8.3 - 4.72 = ☐
10 806 - 392 = ☐	**20** 752 - 514 = ☐	**30** 7.34 - 4.6 = ☐

Exercise 68 Subtraction Practice (Set out in your book)

1 50 - 20 = ☐	**11** 621 - 438 = ☐	**21** 5013 - 4991 = ☐
2 80 - 50 = ☐	**12** 876 - 564 = ☐	**22** 7002 - 6988 = ☐
3 79 - 60 = ☐	**13** 264 - 149 = ☐	**23** 6003 - 5993 = ☐
4 88 - 70 = ☐	**14** 783 - 443 = ☐	**24** 9004 - 8996 = ☐
5 60 - 36 = ☐	**15** 932 - 732 = ☐	**25** 6.8 - 2.9 = ☐
6 90 - 54 = ☐	**16** 345 - 263 = ☐	**26** 2.4 - 1.7 = ☐
7 66 - 45 = ☐	**17** 787 - 524 = ☐	**27** 7.2 - 4.8 = ☐
8 53 - 47 = ☐	**18** 458 - 368 = ☐	**28** 6.8 - 4.93 = ☐
9 400 - 138 = ☐	**19** 690 - 512 = ☐	**29** 7.24 - 3.7 = ☐
10 706 - 492 = ☐	**20** 529 - 398 = ☐	**30** 8.17 - 4.8 = ☐

Name:_____ Date:_____

Exercise 69 Mixed Addition and Subtraction Practice (Set out in your book)

1	52 + 24	= ☐	**11**	279 + 412	= ☐	**21**	421 - 379	= ☐
2	70 - 30	= ☐	**12**	50 - 23	= ☐	**22**	284 + 625	= ☐
3	27 + 41	= ☐	**13**	863 + 291	= ☐	**23**	700 - 273	= ☐
4	59 + 26	= ☐	**14**	72 - 49	= ☐	**24**	496 + 247	= ☐
5	40 - 20	= ☐	**15**	763 + 217	= ☐	**25**	972 + 648	= ☐
6	73 - 60	= ☐	**16**	481 + 279	= ☐	**26**	9.23 + 3.7	= ☐
7	46 + 27	= ☐	**17**	84 - 75	= ☐	**27**	8.4 + 2.74	= ☐
8	69 - 40	= ☐	**18**	324 + 278	= ☐	**28**	854 + 973	= ☐
9	47 + 24	= ☐	**19**	842 - 627	= ☐	**29**	624 + 862	= ☐
10	80 - 23	= ☐	**20**	281 + 463	= ☐	**30**	7.6 + 2.91	= ☐

Exercise 70 Mixed Addition and Subtraction Practice (Set out in your book)

1	70 - 40	= ☐	**11**	69 - 23	= ☐	**21**	500 - 284	= ☐
2	34 + 23	= ☐	**12**	83 - 27	= ☐	**22**	8.7 + 16.2	= ☐
3	30 - 10	= ☐	**13**	279 + 484	= ☐	**23**	862 - 791	= ☐
4	84 - 40	= ☐	**14**	46 - 27	= ☐	**24**	743 - 127	= ☐
5	72 + 12	= ☐	**15**	621 + 735	= ☐	**25**	4.7 + 9.3	= ☐
6	79 - 40	= ☐	**16**	784 + 691	= ☐	**26**	862 - 437	= ☐
7	34 + 46	= ☐	**17**	891 - 423	= ☐	**27**	961 - 729	= ☐
8	80 - 26	= ☐	**18**	726 - 291	= ☐	**28**	6.3 + 7.8	= ☐
9	53 + 28	= ☐	**19**	837 + 724	= ☐	**29**	673 - 268	= ☐
10	70 - 37	= ☐	**20**	429 - 172	= ☐	**30**	4.7 + 2.9	= ☐

Name: _____ **Date:** _____

Exercise 71 Mixed Addition and Subtraction Practice (Set out in your book)

1 63 + 24 = ☐	**11** 324 + 615 = ☐	**21** 573 - 469 = ☐
2 80 - 50 = ☐	**12** 80 - 67 = ☐	**22** 346 + 612 = ☐
3 36 + 52 = ☐	**13** 982 + 645 = ☐	**23** 600 - 346 = ☐
4 64 + 28 = ☐	**14** 63 - 54 = ☐	**24** 362 + 485 = ☐
5 60 - 30 = ☐	**15** 649 + 283 = ☐	**25** 867 + 948 = ☐
6 87 - 50 = ☐	**16** 366 + 149 = ☐	**26** 8.63 - 4.2 = ☐
7 39 + 48 = ☐	**17** 67 - 48 = ☐	**27** 9.03 - 6.13 = ☐
8 74 - 30 = ☐	**18** 494 + 368 = ☐	**28** 8.45 + 2.76 = ☐
9 58 + 33 = ☐	**19** 768 - 427 = ☐	**29** 568 + 437 = ☐
10 90 - 46 = ☐	**20** 398 + 561 = ☐	**30** 18.6 - 13.2 = ☐

Exercise 72 Mixed Addition and Subtraction Practice (Set out in your book)

1 90 - 30 = ☐	**11** 74 - 63 = ☐	**21** 700 - 382 = ☐
2 68 + 54 = ☐	**12** 78 - 39 = ☐	**22** 5.3 + 18.6 = ☐
3 60 - 40 = ☐	**13** 613 + 247 = ☐	**23** 932 - 648 = ☐
4 76 - 30 = ☐	**14** 53 - 37 = ☐	**24** 795 - 148 = ☐
5 36 + 48 = ☐	**15** 654 + 492 = ☐	**25** 342 + 679 = ☐
6 87 - 30 = ☐	**16** 656 + 863 = ☐	**26** 9.48 - 6.25 = ☐
7 48 + 39 = ☐	**17** 862 - 543 = ☐	**27** 76.3 - 52.4 = ☐
8 90 - 27 = ☐	**18** 734 - 512 = ☐	**28** 6.19 + 8.73 = ☐
9 62 + 29 = ☐	**19** 963 + 724 = ☐	**29** 59.2 - 36.1 = ☐
10 80 - 36 = ☐	**20** 873 - 465 = ☐	**30** 27.8 + 54.9 = ☐

Name:_____ Date: _____

Exercise 73 Mixed Addition and Subtraction Practice (Set out in your book)

1	$63 + 21$ =		**11**	$483 + 279$ =		**21**	$704 - 236$ =	
2	$90 - 20$ =		**12**	$63 - 50$ =		**22**	$973 + 821$ =	
3	$46 + 23$ =		**13**	$472 + 693$ =		**23**	$872 - 492$ =	
4	$27 + 49$ =		**14**	$80 - 24$ =		**24**	$683 + 748$ =	
5	$60 - 40$ =		**15**	$843 + 627$ =		**25**	$913 + 648$ =	
6	$76 - 30$ =		**16**	$931 + 734$ =		**26**	$19.6 - 14.21$=	
7	$82 + 76$ =		**17**	$47 - 29$ =		**27**	$8.7 - 6.21$ =	
8	$49 - 20$ =		**18**	$912 + 704$ =		**28**	$2.97 + 6.01$ =	
9	$74 + 29$ =		**19**	$72 - 57$ =		**29**	$3.64 + 8.7$ =	
10	$63 - 30$ =		**20**	$873 + 624$ =		**30**	$7.61 - 6.3$ =	

Exercise 74 Mixed Addition and Subtraction Practice (Set out in your book)

1	$90 - 40$ =		**11**	$90 - 26$ =		**21**	$729 - 461$ =	
2	$27 + 41$ =		**12**	$40 - 17$ =		**22**	$801 + 794$ =	
3	$70 - 20$ =		**13**	$80 + 29$ =		**23**	$817 - 409$ =	
4	$60 - 40$ =		**14**	$90 - 56$ =		**24**	$6.17 - 4.23$ =	
5	$42 + 36$ =		**15**	$974 + 863$ =		**25**	$821 + 672$ =	
6	$54 - 20$ =		**16**	$731 + 482$ =		**26**	$9.72 - 8.27$ =	
7	$27 + 46$ =		**17**	$86 - 27$ =		**27**	$8.63 - 4.71$ =	
8	$82 - 30$ =		**18**	$91 - 36$ =		**28**	$2.01 + 7$ =	
9	$33 + 29$ =		**19**	$763 + 921$ =		**29**	$7.9 - 2.91$ =	
10	$97 - 50$ =		**20**	$86 - 47$ =		**30**	$17.4 + 19.01$=	

Name:_____ Date:_____

Exercise 75 Mixed Addition and Subtraction Practice (Set out in your book)

1	21 + 46 = ☐	**11**	369 + 463 = ☐	**21**	701 - 294 = ☐
2	70 - 30 = ☐	**12**	90 - 36 = ☐	**22**	697 + 836 = ☐
3	36 + 21 = ☐	**13**	724 + 869 = ☐	**23**	796 - 236 = ☐
4	69 + 46 = ☐	**14**	70 - 42 = ☐	**24**	481 + 973 = ☐
5	40 - 20 = ☐	**15**	294 + 397 = ☐	**25**	847 + 294 = ☐
6	59 - 30 = ☐	**16**	317 + 863 = ☐	**26**	8.12 - 7.07 = ☐
7	67 + 83 = ☐	**17**	96 - 27 = ☐	**27**	7.6 - 2.46 = ☐
8	86 - 20 = ☐	**18**	294 + 973 = ☐	**28**	2.71 + 2.07 = ☐
9	48 + 94 = ☐	**19**	63 - 46 = ☐	**29**	7.25 + 8.7 = ☐
10	67 - 40 = ☐	**20**	487 + 921 = ☐	**30**	2.9 - 1.43 = ☐

Exercise 76 Mixed Addition and Subtraction Practice (Set out in your book)

1	70 - 30 = ☐	**11**	80 - 24 = ☐	**21**	700 - 421 = ☐
2	73 + 24 = ☐	**12**	60 - 43 = ☐	**22**	241 + 396 = ☐
3	80 - 60 = ☐	**13**	794 + 872 = ☐	**23**	627 - 486 = ☐
4	90 - 40 = ☐	**14**	70 - 22 = ☐	**24**	872 - 794 = ☐
5	42 + 36 = ☐	**15**	243 + 997 = ☐	**25**	784 + 763 = ☐
6	46 - 20 = ☐	**16**	841 + 781 = ☐	**26**	9.6 - 4.7 = ☐
7	39 + 46 = ☐	**17**	92 - 76 = ☐	**27**	7.4 - 3.12 = ☐
8	83 - 60 = ☐	**18**	46 - 23 = ☐	**28**	7.23 + 6.71 = ☐
9	67 + 87 = ☐	**19**	247 + 693 = ☐	**29**	8.7 - 2.47 = ☐
10	61 - 40 = ☐	**20**	64 - 37 = ☐	**30**	8.9 + 4.27 = ☐

Answers

Exercise 1
1. Example
2. 8 - 80
3. 7 - 70
4. 6 - 60
5. 9 - 90
6. 7 - 70
7. 9 - 90
8. 9 - 90
9. 9 - 90
10. 8 - 80

Exercise 2
1. Example
2. 13 - 130
3. 13 - 130
4. 16 - 160
5. 13 - 130
6. 13 - 130
7. 14 - 140
8. 11 - 110
9. 12 - 120
10. 10 - 100

Exercise 3
1. Example
2. 50
3. 80
4. 40
5. 150
6. 30
7. 180
8. 110
9. 60
10. 140
11. 90
12. 160
13. 200
14. 170
15. 100
16. 120

Exercise 4
1. Example
2. 83
3. 34
4. 98
5. 65
6. 42
7. 156
8. 183
9. 128
10. 162
11. 146
12. 183
13. 157
14. 134
15. 128
16. 175

Exercise 5
1. Example
2. 67
3. 95
4. 95
5. 96
6. 87
7. 89

Exercise 6
1. Example
2. 85
3. 92
4. 90
5. 74
6. 92
7. 72

Exercise 7
1. Example
2. 128
3. 177
4. 168
5. 127
6. 139
7. 123

Exercise 8
1. Example
2. 141
3. 135
4. 156
5. 113
6. 171
7. 153

Exercise 9
1. Example
2. 78
3. 68
4. 89
5. 87
6. 97
7. 87
8. 68
9. 89
10. 69
11. 98
12. 69
13. 88
14. 69
15. 79
16. 89
17. 59
18. 94
19. 59
20. 78
21. 97
22. 89
23. 64

Exercise 10
1. Example
2. 61
3. 71
4. 92
5. 92
6. 91
7. 95
8. 90
9. 92
10. 71
11. 91
12. 91
13. 90
14. 81
15. 81
16. 83
17. 90
18. 92
19. 83
20. 71
21. 91
22. 94
23. 85

Exercise 11
1. Example
2. 109
3. 119
4. 129
5. 125
6. 139
7. 126
8. 139
9. 109
10. 119
11. 119
12. 126
13. 127
14. 115
15. 109
16. 129
17. 119
18. 118
19. 115
20. 117
21. 119
22. 109
23. 117

Exercise 12
1. Example
2. 142
3. 112
4. 111
5. 120
6. 141
7. 124
8. 121
9. 152
10. 141
11. 122
12. 143
13. 130
14. 131
15. 122
16. 143
17. 121
18. 141
19. 144
20. 115
21. 114
22. 134
23. 121

Exercise 13
1. Example
2. 79
3. 95
4. 76
5. 85
6. 69
7. 97
8. 88
9. 87
10. 59
11. 78
12. 97
13. 99
14. 79
15. 79
16. 89
17. 96
18. 89
19. 99
20. 79

Exercise 14
1. Example
2. 84
3. 83
4. 70
5. 76
6. 61
7. 80
8. 80
9. 84
10. 81
11. 95
12. 92
13. 67
14. 82
15. 91
16. 91
17. 84
18. 86
19. 82
20. 92

Exercise 15
1. Example
2. 106
3. 137
4. 129
5. 135
6. 157
7. 139
8. 149
9. 119
10. 128
11. 119
12. 137
13. 118
14. 129
15. 117
16. 119
17. 128
18. 109
19. 127
20. 139

Exercise 16
1. Example
2. 121
3. 132
4. 171
5. 162
6. 133
7. 123
8. 142
9. 130
10. 122
11. 142
12. 110
13. 113
14. 122
15. 121
16. 142
17. 134
18. 151
19. 126
20. 123

Exercise 17
1. Example
2. 878
3. 565
4. 959
5. 687
6. 697
7. 657
8. 998
9. 889
10. 849
11. 999
12. 759

Exercise 18
1. Example
2. 761
3. 884
4. 700
5. 782
6. 890
7. 764
8. 861
9. 986
10. 900
11. 565
12. 793

Exercise 19
1. Example
2. 815
3. 609
4. 804
5. 919
6. 618
7. 729
8. 935
9. 729
10. 617
11. 927
12. 918

Exercise 20
1. Example
2. 507
3. 923
4. 811
5. 932
6. 620
7. 931
8. 432
9. 650
10. 922
11. 741
12. 921

Exercise 21
1. Example
2. 1,186
3. 1,469
4. 1,146
5. 1,195
6. 1,268
7. 1,067
8. 1,179
9. 1,587
10. 1,298
11. 1,448
12. 1,169

Exercise 22
1. Example
2. 1,090
3. 1,204
4. 1,196
5. 1,092
6. 1,483
7. 1,265
8. 1,351
9. 1,202
10. 1,063
11. 1,181
12. 1,063

Exercise 23
1. Example
2. 1,223
3. 1,215
4. 1,416
5. 1,439
6. 1,258
7. 1,217
8. 1,209
9. 1,419
10. 1,405
11. 1,517
12. 1,449

Exercise 24
1. Example
2. 1,623
3. 1,252
4. 1,522
5. 1,221
6. 1,434
7. 1,223
8. 1,323
9. 1,222
10. 1,222
11. 1,141
12. 1,525

Exercise 25
1. Example
2. 8
3. 2
4. 4
5. 6
6. 2
7. 4
8. 6
9. 8
10. 8
11. 9
12. 8
13. 7
14. 6
15. 4
16. 2

Exercise 26
1. Example
2. 5 - 500
3. 6 - 600
4. 2 - 200
5. 3 - 300
6. 3 - 300
7. 3 - 300
8. 2 - 200
9. 2 - 200
10. 2 - 200

Exercise 27
1. Example
2. 2 - 20
3. 5 - 50
4. 5 - 50
5. 3 - 30
6. 3 - 30
7. 4 - 40
8. 2 - 20
9. 4 - 40
10. 2 - 20
11. 3 - 30

Exercise 28
1. Example
2. 4 - 40
3. 8 - 80
4. 7 - 70
5. 3 - 30
6. 7 - 70
7. 7 - 70
8. 3 - 30
9. 7 - 70
10. 7 - 70
11. 7 - 70

Exercise 29
1. Example
2. 20
3. 50
4. 50
5. 40
6. 30
7. 70
8. 20

Exercise 30
1. Example
2. 50
3. 50
4. 20
5. 60
6. 40
7. 40

Exercise 31
1. Example
2. 36
3. 37
4. 29
5. 38
6. 46
7. 28

Exercise 32
1. Example
2. 27
3. 34
4. 37
5. 23
6. 69
7. 33

Exercise 33
1. Example
2. 32
3. 13
4. 34
5. 32
6. 27
7. 16

Exercise 34
1. Example
2. 53
3. 27
4. 17
5. 40
6. 56
7. 48

Exercise 35
1. Example
2. 19
3. 44
4. 48
5. 19
6. 28
7. 17

Exercise 36
1. Example
2. 68
3. 26
4. 57
5. 18
6. 16
7. 27

Exercise 37
1. Example
2. 103
3. 216
4. 164
5. 251
6. 83
7. 140

Exercise 38
1. Example
2. 108
3. 79
4. 116
5. 113
6. 116
7. 72

Exercise 39
1. Example
2. 148
3. 203
4. 121
5. 162
6. 132
7. 191

Exercise 40
1. Example
2. 166
3. 178
4. 134
5. 159
6. 115
7. 119

Exercise 41
1. Example
2. 13
3. 11
4. 23
5. 12
6. 11
7. 18

Exercise 42
1. Example
2. 23
3. 27
4. 24
5. 34
6. 25
7. 25

Exercise 43
1. Example
2. 0.6
3. 2.0
4. 2.4
5. 0.9
6. 1.9
7. 0.6

Exercise 44
1. Example
2. 4.6
3. 7.2
4. 5.2
5. 12.6
6. 7.4
7. 12.9

Exercise 45
1. Example
2. 421
3. 223
4. 111
5. 153
6. 131
7. 313
8. 271
9. 467
10. 264
11. 636
12. 664

Exercise 46
1. Example
2. 314
3. 172
4. 322
5. 351
6. 343
7. 230
8. 212
9. 112
10. 213
11. 321
12. 311

Exercise 47
1. Example
2. 228
3. 329
4. 126
5. 225
6. 249
7. 244
8. 439
9. 125
10. 235
11. 326
12. 219

Exercise 48
1. Example
2. 328
3. 129
4. 228
5. 258
6. 219
7. 338
8. 219
9. 109
10. 115
11. 219
12. 265

Exercise 49
1. Example
2. 393
3. 91
4. 162
5. 51
6. 283
7. 198
8. 190
9. 181
10. 376
11. 191
12. 133

Exercise 50
1. Example
2. 142
3. 171
4. 262
5. 191
6. 222
7. 83
8. 296
9. 262
10. 264
11. 32
12. 273

Exercise 51
1. Example
2. 268
3. 89
4. 179
5. 169
6. 189
7. 166
8. 284
9. 179
10. 188
11. 78
12. 156

Exercise 52
1. Example
2. 165
3. 277
4. 188
5. 179
6. 276
7. 372
8. 178
9. 287
10. 159
11. 178
12. 376

Exercise 53
1. 78
2. 95
3. 96
4. 94
5. 95
6. 85
7. 81
8. 84
9. 89
10. 82
11. 168
12. 129
13. 114
14. 132
15. 151
16. 494
17. 983
18. 699
19. 998
20. 567
21. 656
22. 771
23. 875
24. 864
25. 886
26. 942
27. 1,644
28. 1,669
29. 1,627
30. 1,399

Exercise 54
1. 58
2. 108
3. 59
4. 89
5. 97
6. 100
7. 81
8. 81
9. 100
10. 63
11. 107
12. 102
13. 111
14. 107
15. 124
16. 91
17. 573
18. 468
19. 687
20. 895
21. 702
22. 971
23. 870
24. 1,034
25. 1,521
26. 1,385
27. 1,434
28. 1,203
29. 1,131
30. 1,520

Exercise 55
1. 98
2. 97
3. 68
4. 89
5. 69
6. 91
7. 81
8. 74
9. 64
10. 81
11. 150
12. 118
13. 119
14. 126
15. 104
16. 658
17. 999
18. 589
19. 785
20. 969
21. 475
22. 830
23. 700
24. 1,007
25. 910
26. 1,311
27. 1,109
28. 1,301
29. 1,272
30. 1,404

Exercise 56
1. 93
2. 98
3. 79
4. 98
5. 79
6. 79
7. 100
8. 81
9. 81
10. 92
11. 113
12. 111
13. 94
14. 116
15. 133
16. 588
17. 417
18. 898
19. 949
20. 498
21. 873
22. 601
23. 784
24. 1,001
25. 1,043
26. 1,012
27. 1,200
28. 1,319
29. 1,262
30. 1,041

Exercise 57
1. 59
2. 97
3. 78
4. 95
5. 59
6. 77
7. 92
8. 91
9. 82
10. 71
11. 102
12. 113
13. 111
14. 129
15. 131
16. 589
17. 796
18. 939
19. 878
20. 589
21. 1,012
22. 1,040
23. 1,027
24. 1,224
25. 1,200
26. 1,188
27. 1,179
28. 1,422
29. 1,201
30. 1,376

Exercise 58
1. 79
2. 59
3. 96
4. 59
5. 89
6. 99
7. 81
8. 91
9. 89
10. 81
11. 101
12. 118
13. 102
14. 105
15. 121
16. 879
17. 965
18. 779
19. 876
20. 888
21. 1,009
22. 575
23. 875
24. 1,285
25. 9.6
26. 7.6
27. 14.5
28. 9.1
29. 8.5
30. 6.9

Exercise 59
1. 56
2. 80
3. 57
4. 89
5. 79
6. 71
7. 65
8. 92
9. 54
10. 82
11. 110
12. 104
13. 124
14. 145
15. 130
16. 939
17. 389
18. 786
19. 597
20. 579

Exercise 60
1. 89
2. 98
3. 77
4. 77
5. 59
6. 61
7. 91
8. 81
9. 91
10. 81
11. 117
12. 106
13. 111
14. 100
15. 101
16. 858
17. 687
18. 387
19. 798
20. 597
21. 581
22. 982
23. 881
24. 911
25. 980
26. 1,292
27. 10.15
28. 13.92
29. 11.29
30. 11.09

Exercise 61
1. 50
2. 40
3. 29
4. 46
5. 32
6. 27
7. 48
8. 28
9. 459
10. 314
11. 214
12. 121
13. 131
14. 179
15. 176
16. 588
17. 353
18. 140
19. 451
20. 499
21. 1,013
22. 18
23. 16
24. 34
25. 0.6
26. 4.5
27. 6.5

Additional values from Exercise 60 column:
21. 581
22. 871
23. 571
24. 971
25. 964
26. 1,382
27. 11.01
28. 10.70
29. 12.10
30. 13.77

28. 3.11
29. 1.77
30. 3.33

Exercise 62
1. 30
2. 30
3. 36
4. 52
5. 14
6. 27
7. 27
8. 18
9. 46
10. 363
11. 119
12. 569
13. 124
14. 229
15. 77
16. 477
17. 150
18. 183
19. 261
20. 109
21. 16
22. 18
23. 19
24. 30
25. 6.2
26. 3.6
27. 0.7
28. 5.18
29. 1.79
30. 4.31

Exercise 63
1. 50
2. 40
3. 23
4. 34
5. 28
6. 14
7. 9
8. 17
9. 174
10. 332
11. 248
12. 69
13. 154
14. 124
15. 266
16. 317
17. 151
18. 138
19. 166
20. 151
21. 12
22. 1,006
23. 1,020
24. 1,029
25. 3.5
26. 0.6
27. 5.6
28. 1.97
29. 0.86
30. 2.95

Exercise 64
1. 40
2. 30

3. 28
4. 36
5. 42
6. 14
7. 27
8. 28
9. 35
10. 68
11. 65
12. 109
13. 191
14. 48
15. 203
16. 229
17. 263
18. 179
19. 81
20. 104
21. 15
22. 9
23. 18
24. 20
25. 5.9
26. 6.3
27. 2.4
28. 1.53
29. 6.86
30. 1.08

Exercise 65
1. 20
2. 10
3. 26
4. 28
5. 23
6. 27
7. 21
8. 24
9. 162
10. 134
11. 63
12. 267
13. 69
14. 109
15. 89
16. 235
17. 192
18. 218
19. 111
20. 126
21. 16
22. 31
23. 23
24. 15
25. 2.7
26. 4.9
27. 3.7
28. 2.55
29. 4.44
30. 3.92

Exercise 66
1. 20
2. 20
3. 12
4. 26
5. 11
6. 12
7. 21
8. 16
9. 162

10. 213
11. 190
12. 46
13. 164
14. 58
15. 210
16. 55
17. 213
18. 141
19. 266
20. 139
21. 31
22. 27
23. 5
24. 15
25. 3.0
26. 6.2
27. 5.1
28. 2.72
29. 4.54
30. 5.93

Exercise 67
1. 20
2. 10
3. 49
4. 38
5. 43
6. 11
7. 21
8. 36
9. 62
10. 414
11. 51
12. 204
13. 89
14. 280
15. 172
16. 213
17. 179
18. 263
19. 129
20. 238
21. 5
22. 20
23. 14
24. 21
25. 4.5
26. 1.6
27. 1.9
28. 2.27
29. 3.58
30. 2.74

Exercise 68
1. 30
2. 30
3. 19
4. 18
5. 24
6. 36
7. 21
8. 6
9. 262
10. 214
11. 183
12. 312
13. 115
14. 340
15. 200
16. 82

17. 263
18. 90
19. 178
20. 131
21. 22
22. 14
23. 10
24. 8
25. 3.9
26. 0.7
27. 2.4
28. 1.87
29. 3.54
30. 3.37

Exercise 69
1. 76
2. 40
3. 68
4. 85
5. 20
6. 13
7. 73
8. 29
9. 71
10. 57
11. 691
12. 27
13. 1,154
14. 23
15. 980
16. 760
17. 9
18. 602
19. 215
20. 744
21. 42
22. 909
23. 427
24. 743
25. 1,620
26. 12.93
27. 11.14
28. 1,827
29. 1,486
30. 10.51

Exercise 70
1. 30
2. 57
3. 20
4. 44
5. 84
6. 39
7. 80
8. 54
9. 81
10. 33
11. 46
12. 56
13. 763
14. 19
15. 1,356
16. 1,475
17. 468
18. 435
19. 1,561
20. 257
21. 216
22. 24.9
23. 71

24. 616
25. 14.0
26. 425
27. 232
28. 14.1
29. 405
30. 7.6

Exercise 71
1. 87
2. 30
3. 88
4. 92
5. 30
6. 37
7. 87
8. 44
9. 91
10. 44
11. 939
12. 13
13. 1,627
14. 9
15. 932
16. 515
17. 19
18. 862
19. 341
20. 959
21. 104
22. 958
23. 254
24. 847
25. 1,815
26. 4.43
27. 2.9
28. 11.21
29. 1,005
30. 5.4

Exercise 72
1. 60
2. 122
3. 20
4. 46
5. 84
6. 57
7. 87
8. 63
9. 91
10. 44
11. 11
12. 39
13. 860
14. 16
15. 1,146
16. 1,519
17. 319
18. 222
19. 1,687
20. 408
21. 318
22. 23.9
23. 284
24. 647
25. 1,021
26. 3.23
27. 23.9
28. 14.92
29. 23.1
30. 82.70

Exercise 73
1. 84
2. 70
3. 69
4. 76
5. 20
6. 46
7. 158
8. 29
9. 103
10. 33
11. 762
12. 13
13. 1,165
14. 56
15. 1,470
16. 1,665
17. 18
18. 1,616
19. 15
20. 1,497
21. 468
22. 1,794
23. 380
24. 1,431
25. 1,561
26. 5.39
27. 2.49
28. 8.98
29. 12.34
30. 1.31

Exercise 74
1. 50
2. 68
3. 50
4. 20
5. 78
6. 34
7. 73
8. 52
9. 62
10. 47
11. 64
12. 23
13. 109
14. 34
15. 1,837
16. 1,213
17. 59
18. 55
19. 1,684
20. 39
21. 268
22. 1,595
23. 408
24. 1.94
25. 1,493
26. 1.45
27. 3.92
28. 9.01
29. 4.99
30. 36.41

Exercise 75
1. 67
2. 40
3. 57
4. 115
5. 20
6. 29

7. 150
8. 66
9. 142
10. 27
11. 832
12. 54
13. 1,593
14. 28
15. 691
16. 1,180
17. 69
18. 1,267
19. 17
20. 1,408
21. 407
22. 1,533
23. 560
24. 1,454
25. 1,141
26. 1.05
27. 5.14
28. 4.78
29. 15.95
30. 1.47

Exercise 76
1. 40
2. 97
3. 20
4. 50
5. 78
6. 26
7. 85
8. 23
9. 154
10. 21
11. 56
12. 17
13. 1,666
14. 48
15. 1,240
16. 1,622
17. 16
18. 23
19. 940
20. 27
21. 279
22. 637
23. 141
24. 78
25. 1,547
26. 4.9
27. 4.28
28. 13.94
29. 6.23
30. 13.17